BRAIN BENDERS

CRAZY
CROSSWORDS

Capella

This edition published in 2019 by Arcturus Publishing Limited
26/27 Bickels Yard, 151–153 Bermondsey Street,
London SE1 3HA

Written by Gareth Moore
Illustrations coutesy of Shutterstock

ISBN: 978-1-78888-843-1
CH006940NT
Supplier 10, Date 0319, Print run 8755

Printed in the UK

MIX
Paper from
responsible sources
FSC® C018072
www.fsc.org

CONTENTS

Introduction 6

Puzzles

Beginner 8
    For those who are new to crosswords

Intermediate 44
    Warm up with these puzzles

Expert 80
    Give your brain a real workout

Solutions 116

INTRODUCTION

Welcome to a real hoot of a book, packed full of more than 100 crazy-fun crossword puzzles!

To solve a crossword, just work out the answer to each clue, and then write it in the grid, one letter per square. "Across" clues should be written from left to right, and "down" clues should be written from top to bottom. Start each word at the square that contains a number matching the clue number.

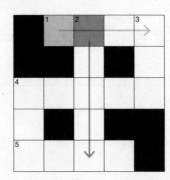

Some clues have a semicolon (";") in them. This breaks the clue into two halves, giving you two entirely separate clues for the same answer, to help you out.

Each clue ends in a number. This tells you how many letters the answer contains, to save you having to count the squares in the grid.

Finally, some clues refer to "anagrams." This means that you need to rearrange the letters in the word you're given. For example, an anagram of "lemon" is "melon."

Good luck!

Beginner

1

ACROSS

1 A word you say to indicate that you can't make a move in a board or card game (4)

4 Respond to an e-mail or letter (5)

5 The period from Monday to Sunday (4)

DOWN

2 Red or green fruit with hard skin and a crunchy middle (5)

3 Blue area above the ground (3)

4 Use oars to move a boat (3)

Beginner

2

ACROSS

1 Large town (4)
3 An entrance hall in a hotel or apartment block (5)
4 Extremely, as in "she was ___ happy" (4)

DOWN

1 If you shut a door then you ___ it (5)
2 A common type of cat with dark stripes (5)

Beginner

3

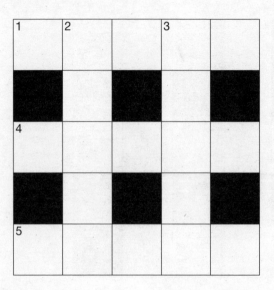

ACROSS

1 Thin branch or twig (5)
4 Quarrel; disagree (5)
5 Not asleep (5)

DOWN

2 Hurl an object, perhaps to another person (5)
3 A noise made by a chicken (5)

4

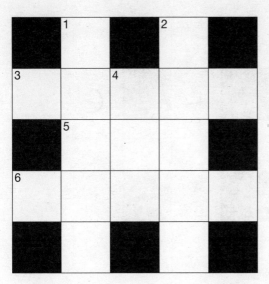

ACROSS

3 Christmas song (5)
5 Somewhere people go to keep fit (3)
6 What you usually do at night (5)

DOWN

1 Very large bird of prey (5)
2 Name of one of Santa's reindeer (5)
4 Cereal, sometimes used in bread and biscuits (3)

Beginner

5

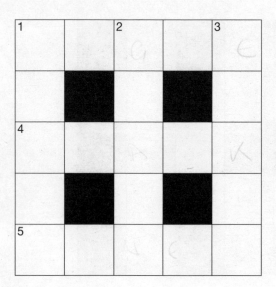

ACROSS

1 Kitchen item used for beating eggs or cream (5)
4 Two times (5)
5 Building you might stay in when away from home (5)

DOWN

1 Woman with magical powers (5)
2 Really silly person (5)
3 What you do when you get down on your knees (5)

6

1 S	■	2 S	■	3 F
4 P	A	P	E	R
A	■	I	■	A
5 D	E	N	I	M
E	■	E	■	E

ACROSS

4 What this book is printed on (5)
5 Cloth used to make jeans (5)

DOWN

1 Tool used for digging (5)
2 Bound edge of a book (5)
3 The edge of a window is called the window ___ (5)

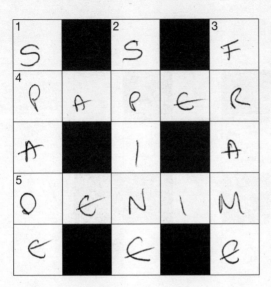

7

	O	G	R	E
		R		E
S	H	A	R	K
O		I		
N	O	N	E	

ACROSS

1 Fairy-tale villain (4)
4 Large sea creature with sharp teeth (5)
5 Not a single one (4)

DOWN

2 Hard cereal seed, such as wheat (5)
3 Screeching sound someone might make if they suddenly see a mouse (3)
4 The male equivalent of "daughter" (3)

Beginner

8

ACROSS

1 A long story on a very big scale (4)
4 At some time in the future (5)
5 Place where a person lives (4)

DOWN

2 Pinkish-yellow juicy fruit with furry skin (5)
3 Thick milk, sometimes added to coffee (5)

Beginner

9

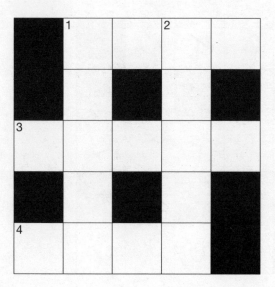

ACROSS

1 A walking track (4)
3 The day between yesterday and tomorrow (5)
4 Flower with a thorny stem, often used in bouquets (4)

DOWN

1 A picture taken with a camera (5)
2 Draw over something onto another sheet of paper on top (5)

Beginner

10

1		2		3
	■		■	
4				
	■		■	
5				

ACROSS

1 Unpleasant sound (5)
4 You might use this for drawing straight lines (5)
5 Very dark wood, once used for black piano keys (5)

DOWN

1 Person trained to look after sick people (5)
2 A house built from blocks of snow (5)
3 What you are if you arrive before the start of an event (5)

Beginner

11

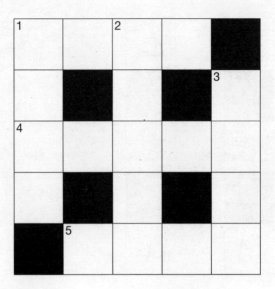

ACROSS

1 Young deer (4)
4 You do this to show that you're happy (5)
5 Listen to something and pay attention (4)

DOWN

1 Quick (4)
2 The opposite of "black" (5)
3 Drop of water from your eye (4)

Beginner

12

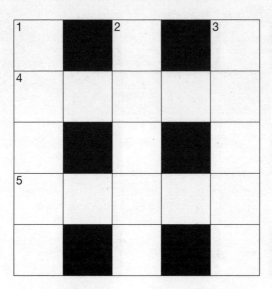

ACROSS

4 The current subject that you're talking about (5)
5 The part of a room you walk on (5)

DOWN

1 Hard; not easy to bend (5)
2 An item worn over the front of the body to protect clothes (5)
3 Long, thin garment worn around the neck to keep you warm (5)

13

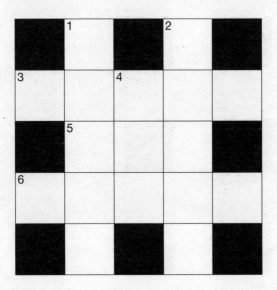

ACROSS

3 Food that's bought in loaves (5)
5 Climbing evergreen plant, sometimes seen attached to buildings (3)
6 Say words (5)

DOWN

1 Catches the foot on something, and then falls forward (5)
2 A type of boat that's very similar to a canoe (5)
4 Biblical couple, Adam and ___ (3)

Beginner

14

ACROSS

1 Young sheep (4)
4 Young adults (5)
5 A dull, continuous pain (4)

DOWN

2 Somewhere sports events take place (5)
3 A long, hard seat for lots of people (5)

15

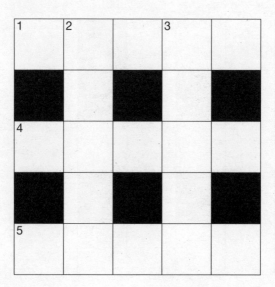

ACROSS

1 The crime of stealing (5)
4 Covered cart that might be pulled by a horse (5)
5 Pay attention, and learn about something, like you might do for a test (5)

DOWN

2 Organ used for pumping blood around the body (5)
3 Natural disaster involving too much water (5)

16

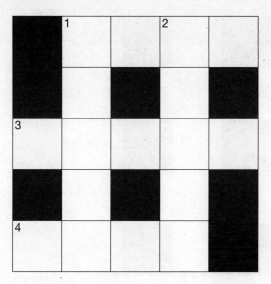

ACROSS

1 Button used to turn the sound off on a TV (4)
3 You stick this on an envelope before you post it (5)
4 A large group of soldiers that fights on land (4)

DOWN

1 A machine that creates movement power (5)
2 A child's word for the stomach (5)

Beginner

17

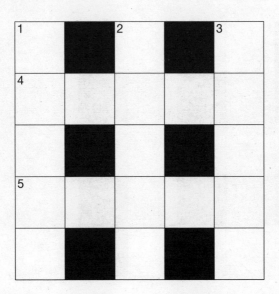

ACROSS

4 Take without permission (5)
5 Not dead (5)

DOWN

1 Common; ordinary (5)
2 This magical being appears when you rub a lamp in some fairy tales (5)
3 If you make a change to something then you ___ it (5)

Beginner

18

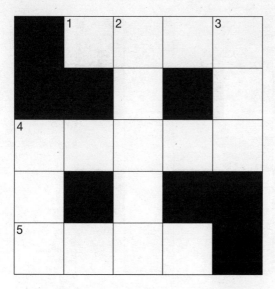

ACROSS

1 Short, thin tree branch (4)
4 Cheerful; happy (5)
5 Male children (4)

DOWN

2 Anxiety; something you are concerned about (5)
3 Informal word for a man (3)
4 Gang or crowd who are unruly, and hard to control (3)

Beginner

19

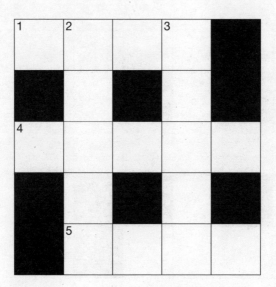

ACROSS

1 Round object often thrown or kicked in games (4)
4 A sphere with a map of the world on it (5)
5 This is often placed next to pepper on a dinner table (4)

DOWN

2 Book of maps (5)
3 Something attached to an item to say who owns it (5)

20

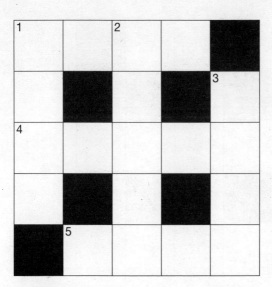

ACROSS

1 Something you might go on at a theme park (4)
4 Circular Italian bread dish (5)
5 Church song (4)

DOWN

1 Very thick string, used for tying up things (4)
2 What you might be after spinning around in circles (5)
3 Unpleasant feeling caused by injury (4)

Beginner

21

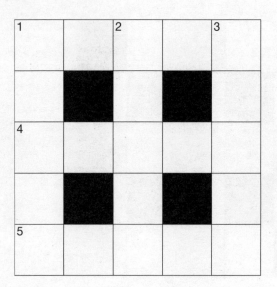

ACROSS

1 A round, flat dish that a meal is served on (5)
4 Informal language (5)
5 Tribal leader (5)

DOWN

1 After you copy some text on a computer, you might ___ it somewhere else (5)
2 A prize given for an achievement (5)
3 Really keen to do something (5)

Beginner

22

ACROSS

3 The central table in a church, where the priest stands (5)
5 Small part of something (3)
6 Someone taught by a teacher (5)

DOWN

1 Book for collecting photos or stamps (5)
2 Ancient Roman language (5)
4 Money you might choose to give to a waiter after a meal (3)

Beginner

23

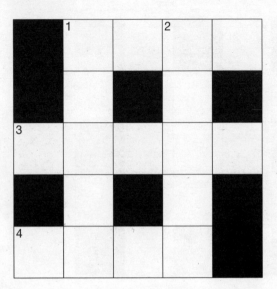

ACROSS

1 Round lump, for example on a camel's back (4)
3 White powder used when making bread (5)
4 The middle of an apple (4)

DOWN

1 Something you say when you meet someone (5)
2 Small, furry animal with a long tail (5)

Beginner

24

	1	2		3
4				
5				

ACROSS

1 Digitally import a paper document into an electronic device (4)
4 Discovered (5)
5 A short message or letter; a musical sound (4)

DOWN

2 The browned edge of a piece of bread (5)
3 Head movement used to signal "yes" (3)
4 Object used to cool yourself (3)

Beginner

25

ACROSS

1 Something that's opened with a key (4)
4 Hair that hangs from a man's chin and cheeks (5)
5 Something that helps you solve a mystery, like a detective might look for (4)

DOWN

1 Rooms used for science experiments (4)
2 Move on hands and knees (5)
3 Sitting around doing nothing (4)

Beginner

ACROSS

1 Get bigger in size (4)
4 If you fall over and cut yourself,
  you might ___ (5)
5 Part of a song sung by just one
  person (4)

DOWN

2 The instructions for a competition
  or event (5)
3 What you turn to steer a
  vehicle (5)

Beginner

27

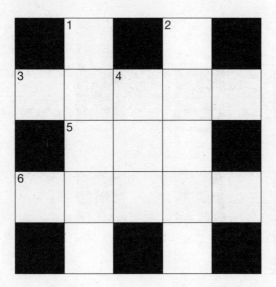

ACROSS

3 Without any clothes on (5)
5 Formal title for a knight (3)
6 A wooden barrier across some land (5)

DOWN

1 An artist uses this to prop up their painting while working (5)
2 Show of kindness and pity (5)
4 Relations; anagram of "ink" (3)

Beginner

28

¹		²		³
	■		■	
⁴				
	■		■	
⁵				

ACROSS

1 Fleecy animal, similar to a small camel without a hump (5)
4 Gather together into sets (5)
5 Narrow one- or two-person paddle boat (5)

DOWN

1 When you think about something and make a deduction, you use ___ (5)
2 Nut from an oak tree (5)
3 Poisoned fruit given to Snow White (5)

Beginner

29

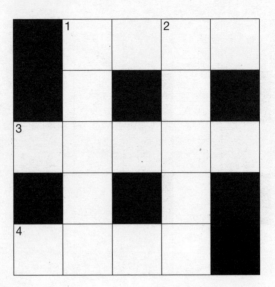

ACROSS

1 A small restaurant or coffee shop (4)
3 A vehicle that pulls carriages along rails (5)
4 Your whole physical being, from head to toes (4)

DOWN

1 Goods carried by a plane or other vehicle (5)
2 Small, winged creature with magic powers, like Tinkerbell (5)

Beginner

30

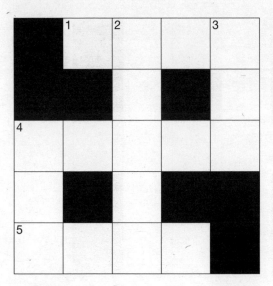

ACROSS

1 The opposite of "shut" (4)
4 Of exactly the same value (5)
5 If you join some friends, you ___ up (4)

DOWN

2 Stop for a short while (5)
3 Nothing; zero (3)
4 Tree whose name is an anagram of "Mel" (3)

Beginner

31

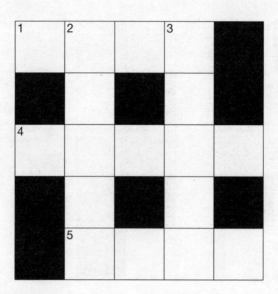

ACROSS

1 Hard covering over a healing cut or graze (4)
4 Flower used for making chains (5)
5 Children play with these (4)

DOWN

2 A detailed plan or map (5)
3 If someone is always ordering other people around for no good reason, they are ___ (5)

Beginner

32

ACROSS

3 The sound that goes with video (5)
5 Number of sides on a die (3)
6 A yellow-and-black striped big cat, found in Asia (5)

DOWN

1 Enjoyable sounds made by instruments or voices (5)
2 Repaired (5)
4 Make a hole in the ground with a spade (3)

Beginner

33

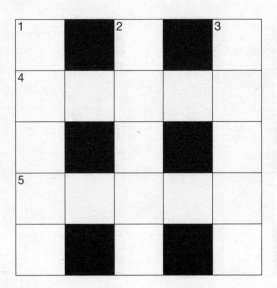

ACROSS

4 Building where a family lives (5)
5 Device that makes a loud warning noise (5)

DOWN

1 Board game with kings, queens, and pawns (5)
2 Someone who protects a place (5)
3 Vegetables that might be green or black (5)

Beginner

34

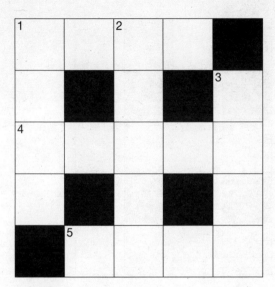

ACROSS

1 The opposite of "hard" (4)
4 A man who is about to be married (5)
5 Male deer; anagram of "tags" (4)

DOWN

1 Road marker that shows which way to go (4)
2 What a piece of wood will usually do on water (5)
3 Feeling too pleased with oneself (4)

Beginner

35

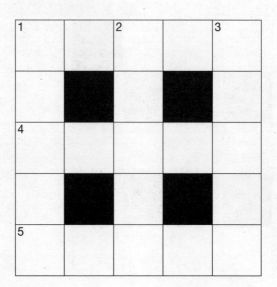

ACROSS

1 Brother of your mother or father (5)
4 Make a serious promise (5)
5 Position between ninth and eleventh (5)

DOWN

1 Anxious; worried (5)
2 Wash in order to remove dirt and stains (5)
3 Our planet (5)

Beginner

36

ACROSS

1 How far down something goes, like water in a swimming pool (5)
4 Another time (5)
5 You would do this to slow down a vehicle (5)

DOWN

2 Enthusiastic; keen (5)
3 Deceive; magician's illusion (5)

ACROSS

1 Teachers in a school (5)
5 Soft candy (7)
6 Green, leafy, salad vegetable (7)
7 Place where milk is processed (5)

DOWN

2 Vehicle used on farms (7)
3 Savage and aggressive (6)
4 You might use this to take photos (6)

Intermediate

38

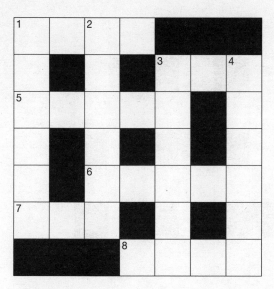

ACROSS

1 Specific day in history; a day marked on a calendar (4)
3 The three states of matter are solid, liquid, and ___ (3)
5 "L"-size clothing (5)
6 Later in time (5)
7 A long, thin stick, such as one used for fishing (3)
8 A casual way of saying "yes" (4)

DOWN

1 More boring (6)
2 Long piece of cotton used for sewing (6)
3 Soft; not rough (6)
4 Look for something (6)

Intermediate

39

ACROSS

1 Voucher (6)
4 First part of the day (7)
6 Pledge that you will do something (7)
8 Number halfway between ten and thirty (6)

DOWN

1 Group of singers (5)
2 Tall, rounded vase (3)
3 Repeatedly bother or scold someone (3)
5 Not very nice at all (5)
6 Deep hole in the ground (3)
7 Grown-up male (3)

Intermediate

40

ACROSS

1 There are two of these at the entrance to your mouth (4)
4 The point at which something stops (3)
6 Useful (7)
7 Heavy unit of weight (3)
8 Famous science-fiction series, "Star ___" (4)

DOWN

2 Small creature with six legs (6)
3 A large snake (7)
5 Multiply by two (6)

Intermediate

41

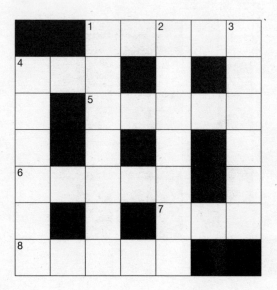

ACROSS

1 Heavenly messenger (5)
4 The closest star to Earth (3)
5 East Asian country with the world's largest population (5)
6 Someone who comes to visit (5)
7 Part of the body used for listening (3)
8 Go into a room, for example (5)

DOWN

1 From a very long time ago (7)
2 Shiny powder used to make things sparkle (7)
3 Someone in charge of a group (6)
4 A music track released on its own, as opposed to being part of an album (6)

Intermediate

42

ACROSS

1 Counting tool with sliding beads (6)
5 Small carpet for wiping your feet on (7)
6 Former NASA vehicle, the "Space ___" (7)
8 Give up work for good (6)

DOWN

2 The opposite of "sister" (7)
3 Motor vehicle (3)
4 Device used for fastening pieces of paper together (7)
7 Very young child (3)

43

ACROSS

1 The sky beyond the atmosphere (5)
5 Loving; loyal (7)
6 Free from prison (7)
7 Woven fabric (5)

DOWN

2 A task you work on for several days (7)
3 A solid, yellowish food made from milk (6)
4 Tell a secret, for example (6)

Intermediate

44

ACROSS

1 The vertical sides of a room (5)
4 Average score on a golf hole (3)
6 Loud breathing noise made during sleep (5)
7 The joint connecting your leg to your foot (5)
8 Spoil, or make something less good; also an anagram of "ram" (3)
9 Not clean (5)

DOWN

1 Knowledge and common sense (6)
2 Big cat with a spotted coat (7)
3 Person who is talking (7)
5 Cure for an illness (6)

Intermediate

45

ACROSS

1 A place where things can be bought (4)
4 What nodding your head usually means (3)
6 Take air in and out of your lungs (7)
7 You can do this on a snowy slope, to move quickly downhill (3)
8 Song sung by two people (4)

DOWN

2 Red playing-card suit (6)
3 Large tomb of ancient Egypt (7)
5 A solid, perfectly round shape (6)

Intermediate

46

ACROSS

3 You use this whenever you lick something (6)
4 Type of fish that looks a bit like a snake (3)
5 New and original; unusual (5)
7 Loud noise (3)
8 Outdoor meal (6)

DOWN

1 Game played on horseback (4)
2 The opposite of "private" (6)
3 Sport played by Rafael Nadal and Venus Williams (6)
6 Make changes to something that's been written (4)

Intermediate

47

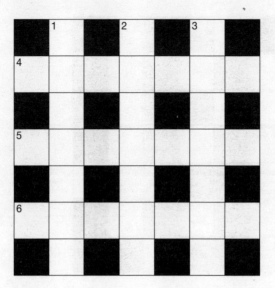

ACROSS

4 Sun umbrella used to provide shade (7)
5 Rub yourself to get rid of an itch (7)
6 Small dried fruit (7)

DOWN

1 Milk contains ___, which is good for bones and teeth (7)
2 Soldiers on horseback (7)
3 Type of mountain that erupts with lava (7)

Intermediate

48

ACROSS

1 Something a witch might cast (5)
5 Take your clothes off (7)
6 Cheaper in price (7)
7 Very hard metal, used for the frames of tall buildings (5)

DOWN

2 Sweet-smelling scent (7)
3 Use your ears (6)
4 Pass on an illness to another person (6)

Intermediate

49

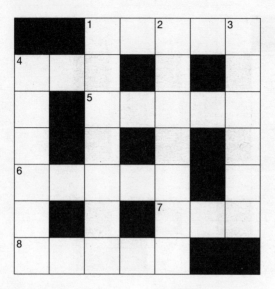

ACROSS

1 Clever; intelligent (5)
4 Large, flightless bird that's native to Australia (3)
5 Device that's like a TV without pictures (5)
6 Large sea creature (5)
7 Secretly watch someone (3)
8 An answer you give, but which you don't know to be correct (5)

DOWN

1 A person's last name (7)
2 Details of where someone lives (7)
3 Decorative cup awarded as a prize (6)
4 Small, crawling insect with pincers (6)

50

ACROSS

1 Portable computer with a built-in keyboard (6)
5 Wanting a drink (7)
6 People belonging to the same family are ___ (7)
8 Short journey to deliver or fetch something for someone else (6)

DOWN

2 Sports player (7)
3 A thick, black liquid used when surfacing streets (3)
4 Repeated visual design (7)
7 The atmosphere all around us (3)

Intermediate

51

ACROSS

2 Find out how many there are of something (5)
4 Fantastic feeling of great happiness (7)
5 Tell someone you think the same thing (5)

DOWN

1 Large bird that eats dead animals (7)
2 Powder used for making chocolate drinks (5)
3 One of the body's five main senses (5)

ACROSS

1 Something you play (4)
3 A word to specify the opposite of something, as in "I will do this, but I will ___ do that" (3)
5 Type of music, particularly popular in the 1970s (5)
6 Underground parts of a tree (5)
7 Something for a child to play with (3)
8 Ancient harp-like instrument (4)

DOWN

1 Small but useful device or tool (6)
2 Great unhappiness (6)
3 No person; no one (6)
4 Absorbent paper used as a handkerchief (6)

Intermediate

53

ACROSS

3 Very smart (6)
4 A part of your body used to see (3)
5 Elected person in charge of a town (5)
7 Make someone annoyed (3)
8 Large, wooden hammer (6)

DOWN

1 Jumping insect that attaches itself to dogs and cats (4)
2 Hidden; not told to others (6)
3 Percussion instrument that looks like a round metal plate (6)
6 On top of; above (4)

Intermediate

54

ACROSS

1 Rough drawing (6)
4 Younger (6)
5 Male parent (6)
6 Say again (6)

DOWN

1 Mix up a deck of playing cards
  ready for a game (7)
2 Biblical letter (7)
3 A flow of water in a river or the
  sea (7)

Intermediate

55

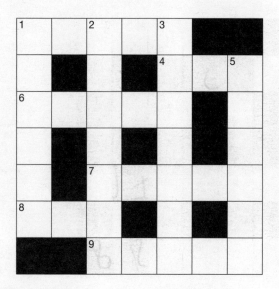

ACROSS

1 Firm and crunchy (5)
4 Knock quickly (3)
6 Incorrect; untrue (5)
7 If you mix yellow and blue paints you get ___ (5)
8 Extended period of time (3)
9 Soup spoon (5)

DOWN

1 Hot drink said to keep you awake (6)
2 Something that is forbidden by law is ___ (7)
3 Imagine something that isn't real (7)
5 Son of a king or queen (6)

56

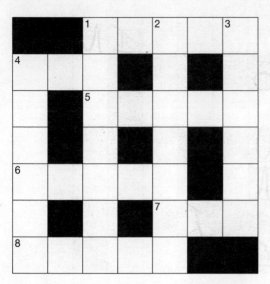

ACROSS

1 Black-and-white bear found in China (5)
4 Hot drink, often brewed from a bag (3)
5 Desert animal with one or two humps and long eyelashes (5)
6 Really surprise (5)
7 Really regret (3)
8 The opposite of "closes" (5)

DOWN

1 Parcel; bundle (7)
2 Quantities; arithmetical values (7)
3 Burning brightly (6)
4 Red fruit often eaten as a vegetable in salad (6)

Intermediate

57

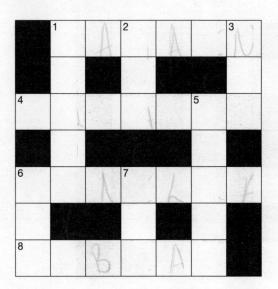

ACROSS

1 Very large group of stars (6)
4 Thin pasta strips often used in Asian food (7)
6 Large seabird with a big pouch in its beak for holding fish (7)
8 To lie down or relax (6)

DOWN

1 Ball-shaped map of the Earth (5)
2 A cover for a jar (3)
3 The opposite of "no" (3)
5 Stay away from (5)
6 Buddy; anagram of "lap" (3)
7 Small hotel (3)

Intermediate

ACROSS

4 Ancient Egyptian paper (7)
5 A deer's horns (7)
6 Frightening creature (7)

DOWN

1 Red, orange, yellow, green, blue, indigo, and violet (7)
2 A very small hair that you find on your eyelid (7)
3 Strong, angry argument (7)

Intermediate

59

ACROSS

1 One more time (5)
5 Living in water (7)
6 Common taste for white ice-cream (7)
7 Black-and-white horselike animal found in Africa (5)

DOWN

2 Slow-moving mass of ice (7)
3 Water dripping from a roof might freeze to make this (6)
4 Shape with four sides of equal length and four right-angles (6)

Intermediate

60

ACROSS

1 Help (6)
5 The bad guy in a story (7)
6 Badly behaved (7)
8 Wanting food (6)

DOWN

2 Leafy, green vegetable that Popeye eats (7)
3 Sick; not well (3)
4 Bird chirp sound (7)
7 Weapon that fires bullets (3)

Intermediate

61

ACROSS

1 Bird's claw (5)
4 The smallest whole number above zero (3)
6 You shed these when you cry (5)
7 Animal that's often ridden (5)
8 A material that's mined for the metal or minerals in it (3)
9 Turns over and over (5)

DOWN

1 Picture permanently inked into the skin (6)
2 Strong material made from cow's skin (7)
3 Nose opening (7)
5 Glowing remains of a fire (6)

62

ACROSS

2 Weapon with a long, pointed blade (5)
4 Long, thin yellow root vegetable (7)
5 The other side, in a battle (5)

DOWN

1 Large, edible seafish with five pairs of limbs (7)
2 Bread that has gone hard is ___ (5)
3 God or goddess (5)

Intermediate

63

ACROSS

1 Clean with water (4)
4 Works of creative imagination (3)
6 Someone who is in the army (7)
7 Sheep's bleat (3)
8 Joy; delight (4)

DOWN

2 Soak up liquid (6)
3 Small case that women often carry with them (7)
5 If you have a dozen eggs, you have this many eggs (6)

Intermediate

64

ACROSS

1 Keen-eyed bird of prey (4)
3 The blackened remains of a fire (3)
5 Clear container for drinking from (5)
6 Huge expanse of water (5)
7 Took part in a sprint race (3)
8 Notice; see (4)

DOWN

1 Further up in the air (6)
2 An item designed for causing harm (6)
3 You are usually in bed with your eyes closed when you are this (6)
4 Large wasp (6)

65

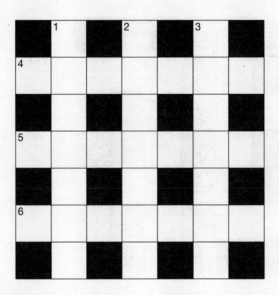

ACROSS

4 Hide (7)
5 Book-lending location (7)
6 Very big, grand house (7)

DOWN

1 Day off work or school (7)
2 A woman who plays a part in a play (7)
3 A person famous for fighting in battle (7)

Intermediate

66

ACROSS

3 Ordinary (6)
4 Playground game where one person chases the rest (3)
5 A strong feeling of fear when you don't know what to do (5)
7 Water drops found on grass in the morning (3)
8 Shiny Christmas decoration (6)

DOWN

1 A relaxation exercise where you hold various body positions (4)
2 Change your mind about doing something; an on-screen button to say "no" to an option (6)
3 Cloth used at mealtimes to wipe your lips (6)
6 Brainwave; clever thought (4)

Intermediate

67

ACROSS

2 Cereal plant used to make flour (5)
4 Place to catch a train (7)
5 Wading bird with long, thin legs (5)

DOWN

1 A, B, and C are ___ (7)
2 Device for measuring time, worn on the wrist (5)
3 Spiky part of a plant (5)

Intermediate

68

ACROSS

1 Clothing for hands, used to keep them warm (6)
4 Young tree that's just been planted (7)
6 Mythical creature with a woman's body and a fish's tail (7)
8 Attractive; nice to look at (6)

DOWN

1 Green or purple fruit that grows on vines (5)
2 Bird that makes a hooting sound (3)
3 Droop to a lower level (3)
5 Unpleasant to listen to (5)
6 Implement used for cleaning floors (3)
7 Came across (someone) (3)

Intermediate

69

ACROSS

1 Dressing that's served with food (5)
5 Pleasant greeting on arrival (7)
6 The process of wearing away by natural forces (7)
7 Prepared to do something (5)

DOWN

2 Charged with a crime, as in "he ___ the man of stealing" (7)
3 Ordinary; usual (6)
4 Unit for measuring temperature (6)

Intermediate

70

ACROSS

1 Time of the evening when it starts to get dark (6)
5 A precious jewel often used to decorate rings (7)
6 Small house in the country (7)
8 A period of sixty seconds (6)

DOWN

2 Fixed set of clothes to be worn to school (7)
3 The result of adding some numbers (3)
4 This evening (7)
7 You might get this from exposing your skin to the sun (3)

Intermediate

ACROSS

3 The area of a rectangle is equal to its width times its ___ (6)
4 Price for doing something (3)
5 Something special that you really enjoy (5)
7 Insect (3)
8 Building where a god is prayed to (6)

DOWN

1 Fast, graceful animal with antlers (4)
2 Large, sculpted model of a person or animal (6)
3 A written message sent by post (6)
6 If you can do something, you are ___ to do it (4)

ACROSS

2 Ice crystals that form on the ground, on walls, and on plants (5)

4 Place where planes take off and land (7)

5 What the sun does during the day (5)

DOWN

1 Small, toothed whale that looks like it has a permanent smile (7)

2 Snack food often served with hamburgers (5)

3 The number of sides a triangle has (5)

Expert

73

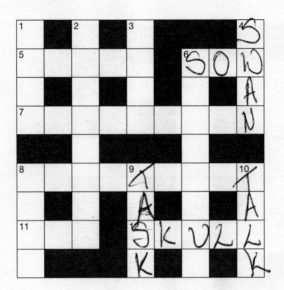

ACROSS

5 Stage show with sung music (5)
6 Plant seed by scattering on the ground (3)
7 Amuse someone (9)
8 Medical care given to a patient (9)
11 Used to exist (3)
12 Head bone (5)

DOWN

1 Romantic feeling (4)
2 Soft covering on a bird (8)
3 The thread-like strands that grow on your head (4)
4 Large, white waterbird with a long neck (4)
6 Disgraceful (8)
8 Area with houses, shops, offices, and buildings (4)
9 A thing that needs to be done (4)
10 Speak; have a conversation (4)

ACROSS

4 Sets out on a yacht (5)
6 Substance used for sticking things together (4)
7 Not tell the truth (3)
9 Short hairs on a man's chin (7)
10 Thick mist (3)
12 Cry of pain (4)
13 Newspapers and television in general (5)

DOWN

1 Able to do something that needs doing (6)
2 Small creature that helps Santa (3)
3 Flower growing on a fruit tree (7)
5 Absolute quiet (7)
8 In a foreign country (6)
11 Precious stone (3)

Expert

75

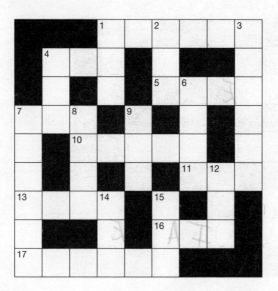

ACROSS

1 Somewhere you might go to see a movie (6)
4 If you travel to and ___, then you are moving forward and backward (3)
5 Birds build this to lay their eggs in (4)
7 Vehicle some children catch to school (3)
10 Still in one piece (5)
11 Something you use to catch fish (3)
13 Unable to feel (4)
16 Young tiger, lion, or bear (3)
17 Modest (6)

DOWN

1 Farmyard animal that produces milk (3)
2 Religious woman who lives in a convent (3)
3 Painter (6)
4 Word that's short for "influenza" (3)
6 Level; not at an angle (4)
7 Tree limb (6)
8 Propel yourself through water (4)
9 Note down quickly (3)
12 When the tide goes out, it is said to ___ (3)
14 Float up and down in water (3)
15 Frozen water (3)

Expert

76

ACROSS

1 A bag with shoulder straps (8)
5 Bundle of paper or soft material (3)
6 You use this both for eating and speaking (5)
8 Fierce storm with strong winds (9)
10 Invisible creature that is said to haunt a place (5)
13 Deity; a being that is prayed to (3)
15 Someone who looks after sheep (8)

DOWN

1 Decorative knot in a ribbon (3)
2 Computer programmer (5)
3 In the past; "it happened long ___" (3)
4 Set of parts to build a model (3)
6 Damp; slightly wet (5)
7 Tool used for removing weeds (3)
8 Squeeze lovingly (3)
9 A rotation between two lines, measured in degrees (5)
11 Male equivalent of "hers" (3)
12 Start legal proceedings against (3)
14 Past tense of "do," as in "this is what I ___ yesterday" (3)

Expert

77

ACROSS

1 Long, soft seat for more than one person, often found in a living room (4)
4 Stolen treasure (4)
7 Region; the space occupied by something (4)
8 An historical fight between two people (4)
9 Sweet spread made with oranges (9)
12 Extremely large (4)
14 Fix something that is broken (4)
16 Group of three; anagram of "riot" (4)
17 Following straight after (4)

DOWN

1 Large expanse of water (3)
2 Something you might set to wake you up in the morning (5)
3 Peas grow in this (3)
5 Common edible fish, often served in sandwiches or a salad (4)
6 Run away (4)
9 Change position (4)
10 Take a break (4)
11 Bitter, yellow fruit; a slice of this is sometimes added to drinks (5)
13 Have a go at an activity (3)
15 A small round mark or spot (3)

Expert

78

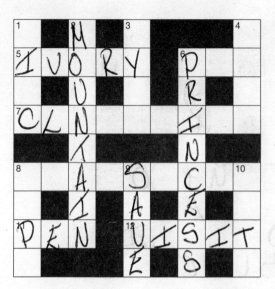

ACROSS

5 White piano keys were once made of this (5)

6 Metal dish with a handle, used for cooking (3)

7 Small, orange fruit (9)

8 To do with the ancient Greeks or Romans (9)

11 Writing device (3)

12 A brief trip to a location (5)

DOWN

1 Thin fog, sometimes seen by water (4)

2 Extremely tall hill (8)

3 Computer memory unit (4)

4 Middle part of your leg (4)

6 Daughter of a king or queen (8)

8 Sleeveless cloak (4)

9 Store a document on a computer (4)

10 Very many (4)

Expert

ACROSS

4 Phones someone (5)
6 Number of sides a rectangle has (4)
7 Period of time during sunlight (3)
9 Edible fish or shellfish (7)
10 Folded and sewn edge of cloth (3)
12 Small medical tablet for swallowing (4)
13 Relating to a king or queen (5)

DOWN

1 What you might do if you saw a ghost (6)
2 Having lived for a long time (3)
3 Kitchen appliance (7)
5 Strapped shoes sometimes worn in summer (7)
8 Two people married to one another (6)
11 Cut grass with a machine (3)

80

ACROSS

1 Silly; ridiculous (6)
4 For each, as in "one ___ person" (3)
5 Symbol used to indicate addition (4)
7 A gorilla, for example (3)
10 Substance injected by snakes (5)
11 Item required to play baseball (3)
13 Entrance lobby in a house (4)
16 Playing card "1" (3)
17 Decoration for a present (6)

DOWN

1 Noah's ship (3)
2 Have a small amount to drink (3)
3 Large area of dry land, often covered in sand (6)
4 Burst, like a balloon (3)
6 An arm or leg (4)
7 Writer (6)
8 Incredibly wicked (4)
9 A word used to refer to one or more of something (3)
12 The length of time you've lived for (3)
14 Throw in a high arc (3)
15 Vehicle for transporting goods (3)

Expert

81

The crossword grid contains the following filled answers:

Row 1: A N C E S T O R
Row 2: I O O U
Row 3: D U B W E I G H
Row 4: R R E
Row 5: G L A D I A T O R
Row 6: A T O
Row 7: P R I C E U R Y
Row 8: O A Z C
Row 9: B U N G A L O W

ACROSS

1 Family relative born before you (8)

5 Re-voice the sound on a film (3)

6 Stand something on scales (5)

8 Roman warrior who fought in public displays (9)

10 The cost of something in a store (5)

13 Slightly mocking, as in "a ___ smile" (3)

15 One-floor house (8)

DOWN

1 Assistance; help (3)

2 Type of venomous snake (5)

3 One of five at the end of your foot (3)

4 Thick floor covering (3)

6 Put words on paper (5)

7 Female equivalent of "his" (3)

8 A space between two things (3)

9 You might dry your face or hands with this (5)

11 Steal something (3)

12 To be able; "I ___ do this" (3)

14 Evergreen tree with red berries (3)

Expert

82

ACROSS

1 You might shout this to ask for urgent assistance (4)

4 Guide people by walking ahead (4)

7 List of restaurant meal options (4)

8 Law (4)

9 Tried (9)

12 Warm and comfortable (4)

14 Press forward (4)

16 Man-made slope (4)

17 Long, deep breath when you are tired (4)

DOWN

1 Cooked meat from a pig (3)

2 Large, soft feather (5)

3 Piece of wood used for rowing (3)

5 Clean; remove dirt from (4)

6 Unwanted plant (4)

9 This as well; too (4)

10 A journey that visits several places (4)

11 Young dog (5)

13 Practical joke (3)

15 Female bird (3)

ACROSS

5 Animal used for pulling carriages (5)
6 You use this to look at the world around you (3)
7 Moving staircase (9)
8 Device used for reheating food (9)
11 That girl; her (3)
12 Chocolate powder (5)

DOWN

1 Outer covering for your foot (4)
2 Vehicle with three wheels (8)
3 Breakfast, lunch, or dinner, for example (4)
4 It might be grizzly, polar, or teddy (4)
6 The opposite of "exit" (8)
8 Decorative face covering (4)
9 Fairy-tale beginning, "___ upon a time" (4)
10 Formal educational test (4)

Expert

84

ACROSS

4 Supernatural powers (5)
6 Hold on to (4)
7 Wet, muddy area of ground (3)
9 Mothers and fathers (7)
10 Take advantage of (3)
12 Cry about something really sad (4)
13 A piece of furniture with legs and a flat top (5)

DOWN

1 Group of countries under one ruler (6)
2 The tip of a pen (3)
3 Violent storm; also the name of a play by Shakespeare, "The ___" (7)
5 Small mat to place under a mug or cup (7)
8 Reply to a question (6)
11 Chew food and swallow (3)

Expert

85

ACROSS

1 Triangular Indian snack (6)
4 A wooden object used for hitting a ball (3)
5 Pull something heavy (4)
7 Commercial messages (3)
10 Italian noodles (5)
11 Did light, as in "I ___ the candle" (3)
13 A solemn promise, as might be sworn on a Bible (4)
16 Music with fast, spoken lyrics (3)
17 Spread made by churning milk (6)

DOWN

1 Place where pigs live (3)
2 Crazy; not sane (3)
3 The eighth month of the year (6)
4 The opposite of "good" (3)
6 Not imaginary (4)
7 Take in and understand (6)
8 Distinctive Dalmatian feature (4)
9 Request (3)
12 Cheeky devil (3)
14 Something which has been a big success (3)
15 Do something wrong (3)

Expert

ACROSS

1 Heavenly place (8)
6 Something from East Asian countries, like Japan or China (8)
9 Food plant (9)
13 Was curious about something (8)
16 Game with dotted tiles representing numbers (8)

DOWN

2 Higher up than (5)
3 Living; existing (5)
4 Place to spend the night (3)
5 Period of time; anagram of "are" (3)
7 Small flap used to mark a page (3)
8 Tell a fib (3)
9 Solemn promise (3)
10 A pistol, for example (3)
11 Cook's protective garment (5)
12 Deep spoon with a long handle, often used to serve soup (5)
14 The opposite of "even" (3)
15 Faintly lit (3)

Expert

87

ACROSS

1 Machine for carrying people or goods (7)
6 Place where scientists work (3)
7 Doctor's assistant (5)
8 Someone who travels into space (9)
10 A camel-like animal; anagram of "a mall" (5)
12 We breathe this to stay alive (3)
13 Character of the alphabet that isn't a vowel (7)

DOWN

1 Extremely useful or important (8)
2 Something people find it hard to avoid doing, like chewing their nails, for example (5)
3 A letter of the alphabet that isn't a vowel (9)
4 You use this to hear (3)
5 False teeth (8)
9 Not sleeping (5)
11 The entire quantity of something (3)

Expert

88

ACROSS

5 Exactly right (5)
6 Planned for a certain time (3)
7 High-ranking teacher (9)
8 Model person used to keep birds away from crops (9)
11 Enemy (3)
12 A stand used by an artist while painting (5)

DOWN

1 Walk with difficulty, as you might do if you twisted your ankle (4)
2 Make something look more attractive by adding to it (8)
3 A hint (4)
4 Orchard fruit that's wider at the base than at the top (4)
6 Sorrow; upset (8)
8 Somewhere secure to store valuables (4)
9 You see the world using these (4)
10 Little Red Riding Hood was very afraid of the Big Bad ___ (4)

Expert

89

ACROSS

1 At a comfortably high temperature (4)
4 Absent from home (4)
7 Way out (4)
8 Black substance that's mined, and used for fuel (4)
9 Bad dream (9)
12 Gentle; not hard (4)
14 Sleep lightly; nap (4)
16 Large brass instrument (4)
17 Piece of string used to tie a shoe (4)

DOWN

1 Great distress (3)
2 Small stick struck to create a flame (5)
3 McDonald's burger, Big ___ (3)
5 Spiritual and physical relaxation technique (4)
6 Great delight (4)
9 The part of the face used for smelling (4)
10 A present bought for a person (4)
11 Prize given for bravery, or for winning something (5)
13 Hard pull (3)
15 Female sheep (3)

Expert

90

ACROSS

1 Event where something bad happens by chance (8)
5 You sing into this for karaoke (3)
6 Someone from another planet (5)
8 Strong, spinning column of air (9)
10 Unpleasant; horrible (5)
13 Place down (3)
15 Very big (8)

DOWN

1 Point at a target (3)
2 Spiky plants found in the desert (5)
3 Snake-shaped fish (3)
4 Something a man might wear with a shirt (3)
6 Narrow street or passageway (5)
7 Head motion used for agreeing (3)
8 Succeeded at a competition, perhaps (3)
9 Inuit's house (5)
11 Had dinner, maybe (3)
12 Also; as well (3)
14 Word used for agreeing (3)

91

ACROSS

4 Poisonous (5)
6 Small, jumping insect (4)
7 Definite article, as in "that's ___ one that I want" (3)
9 Invisible line marking halfway between the North and South Poles (7)
10 Cooked pig's meat (3)
12 An adult might do this to remove creases from clothing (4)
13 Language of the ancient Romans (5)

DOWN

1 Facebook posting, perhaps (6)
2 Healthy; strong (3)
3 Against the law (7)
5 Horse-drawn carriage used for racing (7)
8 Thin rope used for tying things (6)
11 Month between April and June (3)

Expert

92

ACROSS

1 Part of the eye; flower (4)
4 Did own, as in "I ___ that" (3)
5 Circular type of chart (3)
6 Stitch together (3)
8 Dog rope (5)
9 It's found between your shoulder and your hand (3)
10 Nocturnal bird of prey (3)
11 Joint of the body (5)
13 Very warm (3)
15 December 24th is Christmas ___ (3)
16 Period of fighting between armies (3)
17 Call a phone number (4)

DOWN

1 Concept (4)
2 Try to get money from someone through a legal process; a girl's name (3)
3 If you jump into a swimming pool, you will make a ___ (6)
4 Hard hat used to protect the head (6)
6 Light rain that lasts for a short time (6)
7 Pocket-sized money case (6)
12 Deep, round dish (4)
14 Strange; unusual (3)

Expert

93

ACROSS

1 Owns (3)
3 Let someone do something; permit (5)
6 Juicy, tropical fruit with yellow flesh (5)
7 Public-transport vehicle (3)
8 Long word for "spying"; the use of spies (9)
9 The highest part of something (3)
10 Foolish person (5)
12 Think the same as someone else (5)
13 Short sleep (3)

DOWN

1 Sing with closed lips (3)
2 Rough sheet used to smooth wood (9)
3 Say sorry (9)
4 Someone who helps you borrow books (9)
5 Leftover parts; items that are not used (5)
8 A minor actor who doesn't speak (5)
11 Gentle touch (3)

Expert

94

The completed grid (handwritten answers):

T	H	I	R	S	T	Y
O		M	P		E	P
B	A	A	A	C	T	O R
O		G	G			E
G	R	E	H	O U	N	D
M			E	P		I
A	G	E N	T	S E	T	
N	G	T		E		O
	G	L	I T M E	R

ACROSS

1 In need of water (7)

6 Sound made by a sheep (3)

7 Person in a play (5)

8 Slim dog, often used for racing (9)

10 Someone who looks after a celebrity, and finds them jobs (5)

12 A group of related items (3)

13 Sparkle (7)

DOWN

1 Sled for sliding downhill (8)

2 Picture (5)

3 Long, stringy pasta (9)

4 Up until now, as in "I haven't told anyone ___" (3)

5 Animal that hunts other animals (8)

9 Make someone unhappy (5)

11 Shelled food often eaten fried, scrambled, or boiled (3)

ACROSS

1 Difficult, like a tricky problem (4)
4 The underground part of a plant (4)
7 A single step (4)
8 Something by which a person is called (4)
9 Group of people living in one place (9)
12 Object used on stage in a play (4)
14 The sight from a particular place (4)
16 Cubes with sides numbered from one to six (4)
17 Precious red stone (4)

DOWN

1 Joint between the thigh and pelvis (3)
2 While you're asleep, you might have a ___ (5)
3 Male child (3)
5 Hired transport vehicle (4)
6 To a great degree (4)
9 Make a duplicate of something (4)
10 The way you feel (4)
11 At no time in the past or future (5)
13 Small seed found in fruit (3)
15 For what reason? (3)

Expert

96

ACROSS

5 Once more (5)
6 Uncooked (3)
7 Flash during a thunderstorm (9)
8 Short-tailed game bird (9)
11 "Once upon a time, a long time ___" (3)
12 Classic game played on a black-and-white board (5)

DOWN

1 The hard part at the end of your finger (4)
2 Australian animal that moves by jumping (8)
3 Deliberate tangle in a piece of string or rope (4)
4 Woody shoot on a tree branch (4)
6 "Rudolph the Red-nosed ___" (8)
8 Take part in a game (4)
9 Competition to arrive first (4)
10 Simple difficulty level (4)

Expert

97

ACROSS

1 Burn a surface (6)
4 Wonder (3)
5 Narrow (4)
7 Which person? (3)
10 Large area of flat land with few trees (5)
11 Obtained (3)
13 Small horse (4)
16 Mourn; repent (3)
17 The countryside in general (6)

DOWN

1 Large body of salt water (3)
2 Choose; anagram of "top" (3)
3 Trustworthy (6)
4 Type of tree; anagram of "has" (3)
6 The Christmas decorations were ___ on the tree (4)
7 Something used to in battle (6)
8 Ready for business, especially if a shop (4)
9 Dry grass used as food for animals (3)
12 Need to give money to someone (3)
14 A person, not me (3)
15 Mineral-bearing rock (3)

Expert

ACROSS

4 Reasoning that makes sense (5)
6 Not costing anything (4)
7 Deep, round container (3)
9 Unusual; different (7)
10 Word sometimes used to close a story, as in "The ___" (3)
12 Rear surface (4)
13 The overall amount (5)

DOWN

1 Intelligent (6)
2 Briefly place something into a liquid, and then take it back out (3)
3 You might receive this at Christmas (7)
5 Try to form a set of things, such as stamps, or stickers (7)
8 Eat in small bites (6)
11 Canine animal (3)

Expert

ACROSS

1 Device used to heat a room (8)
5 Forbid something (3)
6 These crash onto a beach (5)
8 Tree that stays in leaf all year long (9)
10 High body temperature (5)
13 Slang term for police officer (3)
15 Device used to keep you dry during rain (8)

DOWN

1 Move something back and forth against something else, as Aladdin did to make the genie appear (3)
2 Waltz or tango, for example (5)
3 Hot or iced drink (3)
4 Fish eggs (3)
6 Bet (5)
7 Break a law, especially a religious one (3)
8 Dobby, in "Harry Potter" (3)
9 Perform exceptionally well (5)
11 Large, ostrich-like bird (3)
12 Tidal movement away from the land; flow back (3)
14 Podded vegetable (3)

Expert

100

ACROSS

1 Swimming-pool game, water ___ (4)

4 The home of Winnie the Pooh is the Hundred ___ Wood (4)

7 Where spiders live (4)

8 Melody (4)

9 What you're solving at this very moment (9)

12 Word that means "the two together" (4)

14 Written words (4)

16 Team, as in "Which ___ are you on?" (4)

17 Strong anger; anagram of "gear" (4)

DOWN

1 Wooden church bench (3)

2 Green place in a desert (5)

3 Drawings, paintings, sculptures, and music (3)

5 The name of the currency used in most European countries (4)

6 Give food to a person (4)

9 A die is this type of six-sided, three-dimensional shape (4)

10 Cereal commonly used for food (4)

11 When it rains, ___ falls from the sky (5)

13 The opposite of "her" (3)

15 Foot digit (3)

Expert

101

ACROSS

5 At a higher level than (5)
6 Number not wholly divisible by two (3)
7 A beauty or health care activity (9)
8 Exactly the same (9)
11 Boy (3)
12 Stick something in place (5)

DOWN

1 Some (but not all) of something (4)
2 The region above your eyebrows (8)
3 Examination (4)
4 Make changes (4)
6 Covered with cloud (8)
8 Lazy, perhaps (4)
9 Sticky material on a roll (4)
10 Didn't tell the truth (4)

Expert

102

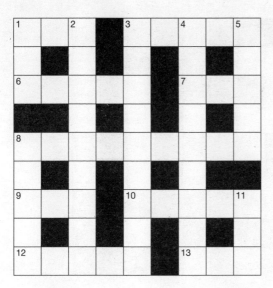

ACROSS

1 Soft, flat hat (3)
3 Thick milk (5)
6 Bamboo-eating animal (5)
7 A pile of blank paper fastened together in a book (3)
8 Poisonous, mushroom-like plant (9)
9 Mischievous child (3)
10 Young bird (5)
12 A particular scent (5)
13 Fruit with a hard shell (3)

DOWN

1 Small drinking container (3)
2 Large tropical fruit with tough, spiky skin (9)
3 Type of music composed by people such as Mozart (9)
4 Big, noisy bang (9)
5 Someone who poses for photos (5)
8 Excursions (5)
11 Set of pieces to assemble (3)

ACROSS

1 Picture puzzle requiring assembly (6)
4 Illness often caught in the winter (3)
5 Graceful, white waterbird (4)
7 The opposite of "hi" (3)
10 Small, venomous snake (5)
11 At this time (3)
13 A man crowned as a ruler (4)
16 Operate, as in "I will ___ the car" (3)
17 Angry mood (6)

DOWN

1 Deep container for liquid (3)
2 Oxygen or hydrogen, for example (3)
3 Opening in a wall (6)
4 Small, black, airborne insect (3)
6 Tell someone about a danger (4)
7 Hoop target in a team sport (6)
8 Wholly divisible by two, as a number (4)
9 Large, tailless monkey (3)
12 A single item (3)
14 A space or interval (3)
15 Soft covering on a dog or other animal (3)

104

ACROSS

4 Room just under the roof of a house (5)
6 Selfish; not generous (4)
7 Speak out loud (3)
9 Large African ape (7)
10 Cunning and mischievous, as a fox is often said to be (3)
12 Take hold of something roughly (4)
13 React to a joke, perhaps (5)

DOWN

1 Animal dung used on the land (6)
2 That man's or boy's (3)
3 Common beach bird (7)
5 Large group of people, vehicles, and animals (7)
8 Aircraft journey (6)
11 Sharp barking sound (3)

Expert

105

ACROSS

1 Unhappy; sad (4)
4 Individual article or unit (4)
7 Brightest object in the sky at night (4)
8 A unit of computer memory storage (4)
9 Animal's footwear, used as a sign of good luck (9)
12 What a red light on a traffic signal tells you to do (4)
14 Very straightforward (4)
16 Not very nice to other people (4)
17 Earth; soil (4)

DOWN

1 The pink flesh around your teeth (3)
2 Sign used to indicate subtraction (5)
3 Spider's home (3)
5 Traditional story about gods and heroes (4)
6 At this place (4)
9 You say this to ask people to be quiet (4)
10 Kitchen or hall, for example (4)
11 Use money to buy something (5)
13 Pin for hanging things on (3)
15 Annoying travel question: "Are we there ___?" (3)

Expert

106

ACROSS

1 Heavy fall of rain (8)
5 Shout of disapproval (3)
6 Mix together smoothly (5)
8 Autograph (9)
10 An elephant's nose (5)
13 Pull one vehicle with another (3)
15 *Tyrannosaurus rex* or *Stegosaurus*, for example (8)

DOWN

1 Touch gently with a tissue, perhaps to clean or dry (3)
2 Incorrect (5)
3 It might be sunflower or olive, and is used in cooking (3)
4 A fast jog (3)
6 Not yet written on (5)
7 Needing to be paid (3)
8 Rest on a chair (3)
9 A word prefix that means "extremely" (5)
11 Fisherman's stick (3)
12 Religious woman (3)
14 Armed conflict (3)

Expert

107

ACROSS

5 A king or queen, for example (5)
6 A long way (3)
7 Citrus fruit preserve (9)
8 Small, orange-like fruit (9)
11 A light touch of the hand (3)
12 Disagree (5)

DOWN

1 Cut away unwanted parts with scissors, for example (4)
2 Woodwind instrument (8)
3 Measurement that (for a rectangle) is equal to width times length (4)
4 Large plant with a trunk (4)
6 Pink, tropical wading bird (8)
8 Kind; sort (4)
9 Academic test (4)
10 Adam and Eve's garden (4)

Expert

108

ACROSS

1 Insects (4)
4 Going through; stopping at (3)
5 Have a need to pay something back (3)
6 A fish uses this to swim (3)
8 Cowboy contest (5)
9 Male sheep (3)
10 Throw (3)
11 Perfect (5)
13 Looking tired or pale (3)
15 Advanced in years (3)
16 How meat is before it is cooked (3)
17 The opposite of "short" (4)

DOWN

1 Not having any hair (4)
2 Narrow runner for use on snow (3)
3 Sadness (6)
4 Unwanted animals that cause problems (6)
6 Travel behind someone (6)
7 Not a single person (6)
12 British nobleman (4)
14 Take part in a play (3)

CRAZY
CROSSWORDS

SOLUTIONS

Solutions

1

```
. P A S S
. P . K .
R E P L Y
O . L . .
W E E K .
```

2

```
. C I T Y
. L . A .
L O B B Y
. S . B .
V E R Y .
```

3

```
S T I C K
. H . L .
A R G U E
. O . C .
A W A K E
```

4

```
. E . C .
C A R O L
. G Y M .
S L E E P
. E . T .
```

5

```
W H I S K
I . D . N
T W I C E
C . O . E
H O T E L
```

6

```
S . S . F
P A P E R
A . I . A
D E N I M
E . E . E
```

7

```
. O G R E
. R . E .
S H A R K
O . I . .
N O N E .
```

8

```
E P I C .
. E . R .
L A T E R
. C . A .
. H O M E
```

9

```
. P A T H
. H . R .
T O D A Y
. T . C .
R O S E .
```

Solutions

10

N	O	I	S	E
U		G		A
R	U	L	E	R
S		O		L
E	B	O	N	Y

11

F	A	W	N	
A		H		T
S	M	I	L	E
T		T		A
	H	E	A	R

12

S		A		S
T	O	P	I	C
I		R		A
F	L	O	O	R
F		N		F

13

	T		K	
B	R	E	A	D
	I	V	Y	
S	P	E	A	K
	S		K	

14

L	A	M	B	
	R		E	
T	E	E	N	S
	N		C	
	A	C	H	E

15

T	H	E	F	T
	E		L	
W	A	G	O	N
	R		O	
S	T	U	D	Y

16

	M	U	T	E
	O		U	
S	T	A	M	P
	O		M	
A	R	M	Y	

17

U		G		A
S	T	E	A	L
U		N		T
A	L	I	V	E
L		E		R

18

	T	W	I	G
	O		O	
M	E	R	R	Y
O		R		
B	O	Y	S	

Solutions

19

B	A	L	L	
	T		A	
G	L	O	B	E
	A		E	
	S	A	L	T

20

R	I	D	E	
O		I		P
P	I	Z	Z	A
E		Z		I
	H	Y	M	N

21

P	L	A	T	E
A		W		A
S	L	A	N	G
T		R		E
E	L	D	E	R

22

	A		L	
A	L	T	A	R
	B		I	T
P	U	P	I	L
	M		N	

23

	H	U	M	P
	E		O	
F	L	O	U	R
	L		S	
C	O	R	E	

24

	S	C	A	N
		R		O
F	O	U	N	D
A		S		
N	O	T	E	

25

L	O	C	K	
A		R		I
B	E	A	R	D
S		W		L
	C	L	U	E

26

G	R	O	W	
	U		H	
B	L	E	E	D
	E		E	
	S	O	L	O

27

	E		M	
N	A	K	E	D
	S		I	R
F	E	N	C	E
	L		Y	

Solutions

28

L	L	A	M	A
O		C		P
G	R	O	U	P
I		R		L
C	A	N	O	E

29

	C	A	F	E
	A		A	
T	R	A	I	N
	G		R	
B	O	D	Y	

30

	O	P	E	N
		A		I
E	Q	U	A	L
L		S		
M	E	E	T	

31

S	C	A	B	
	H		O	
D	A	I	S	Y
	R		S	
	T	O	Y	S

32

	M		F	
A	U	D	I	O
	S	I	X	
T	I	G	E	R
	C		D	

33

C		G		B
H	O	U	S	E
E		A		A
S	I	R	E	N
S		D		S

34

S	O	F	T	
I		L		S
G	R	O	O	M
N		A		U
	S	T	A	G

35

U	N	C	L	E
P		L		A
S	W	E	A	R
E		A		T
T	E	N	T	H

36

D	E	P	T	H
	A		R	
A	G	A	I	N
	E		C	
B	R	A	K	E

Solutions

37

	S	T	A	F	F
	C		R		I
C	A	R	A	M	E	L
	M		C		R
L	E	T	T	U	C	E
	R		O		E
D	A	I	R	Y	

38

D	A	T	E		
U		H		G	A	S
L	A	R	G	E		E
L		E		N		A
E		A	F	T	E	R
R	O	D		L		C
			Y	E	A	H

39

	C	O	U	P	O	N
	H		R		A
M	O	R	N	I	N	G
	I				A
P	R	O	M	I	S	E
I			A		T
T	W	E	N	T	Y

40

L	I	P	S		
	N		E	N	D
	S		R		O
H	E	L	P	F	U	L
	C		E		B
	T	O	N		L
			T	R	E	K

41

	A	N	G	E	L
S	U	N		L		E
I		C	H	I	N	A
N		I		T		D
G	U	E	S	T		E
L		N		E	A	R
E	N	T	E	R	

42

A	B	A	C	U	S
	R		A		T
D	O	O	R	M	A	T
	T				P
S	H	U	T	T	L	E
	E		O		E
	R	E	T	I	R	E

43

	S	P	A	C	E
	R		R		H
D	E	V	O	T	E	D
	V		J		E
R	E	L	E	A	S	E
	A		C		E
C	L	O	T	H	

44

W	A	L	L	S	
I		E		P	A	R
S	N	O	R	E		E
D		P		A		M
O		A	N	K	L	E
M	A	R		E		D
	D	I	R	T	Y

45

S	H	O	P		
	E		Y	E	S
	A		R		P
B	R	E	A	T	H	E
	T		M		E
	S	K	I		R
		D	U	E	T

Solutions

46

	P			P	
T	O	N	G	U	E
E	E	L		B	
	N	O	V	E	L
	N		D	I	N
P	I	C	N	I	C
	S			T	

47

	C		C		V	
P	A	R	A	S	O	L
	L		V		L	
S	C	R	A	T	C	H
	I		L		A	
C	U	R	R	A	N	T
	M		Y		O	

48

		S	P	E	L	L
	I		E		I	
U	N	D	R	E	S	S
	F		F		T	
R	E	D	U	C	E	D
	C		M		N	
S	T	E	E	L		

49

		S	M	A	R	T
E	M	U		D		R
A		R	A	D	I	O
R		N		R		P
W	H	A	L	E		H
I		M		S	P	Y
G	U	E	S	S		

50

L	A	P	T	O	P	
	T		A		A	
T	H	I	R	S	T	Y
	L				T	
R	E	L	A	T	E	D
	T		I		R	
	E	R	R	A	N	D

51

			V			
	C	O	U	N	T	
	O		L		A	
E	C	S	T	A	S	Y
	O		U		T	
A	G	R	E	E		
			E			

52

G	A	M	E			
A		I		N	O	T
D	I	S	C	O		I
G		E		B		S
E		R	O	O	T	S
T	O	Y		D		U
			L	Y	R	E

53

		F			S	
	C	L	E	V	E	R
E	Y	E			C	
	M	A	Y	O	R	
	B			V	E	X
M	A	L	L	E	T	
	L			R		

54

	S	K	E	T	C	H
	H		P		U	
J	U	N	I	O	R	
	F		S		R	
	F	A	T	H	E	R
	L		L		N	
R	E	P	E	A	T	

Solutions

55

C	R	I	S	P		
O		L		R	A	P
F	A	L	S	E		R
F		E		T		I
E		G	R	E	E	N
E	R	A		N		C
		L	A	D	L	E

56

		P	A	N	D	A
T	E	A		U		B
O		C	A	M	E	L
M		K		B		A
A	M	A	Z	E		Z
T		G		R	U	E
O	P	E	N	S		

57

	G	A	L	A	X	Y
	L		I			E
N	O	O	D	L	E	S
	B				V	
P	E	L	I	C	A	N
A		N			D	
L	O	U	N	G	E	

58

	R		E		Q	
P	A	P	Y	R	U	S
	I		E		A	
A	N	T	L	E	R	S
	B		A		R	
M	O	N	S	T	E	R
	W		H		L	

59

	A	G	A	I	N
	S		L		C
A	Q	U	A	T	I	C
U		C		C	
V	A	N	I	L	L	A
R		E		E	
Z	E	B	R	A	

60

A	S	S	I	S	T	
	P		L		W	
V	I	L	L	A	I	N
	N				T	
N	A	U	G	H	T	Y
	C		U		E	
H	U	N	G	R	Y	

61

T	A	L	O	N	
A		E		O	N	E
T	E	A	R	S		M
T		T		T		B
O		H	O	R	S	E
O	R	E		I		R
	R	O	L	L	S

62

		L		
S	W	O	R	D
T		B		E
P	A	R	S	N	I	P
L		T		T
E	N	E	M	Y
	R

63

W	A	S	H	
	B		A	R	T
	S		N		W
S	O	L	D	I	E	R
	R		B		L
B	A	A		V
		G	L	E	E

Solutions

64

H	A	W	K			
I		E		A	S	H
G	L	A	S	S		O
H		P		L		R
E		O	C	E	A	N
R	A	N		E		E
		S	P	O	T	

65

	H		A		W	
C	O	N	C	E	A	L
	L		T		R	
L	I	B	R	A	R	Y
	D		E		I	
M	A	N	S	I	O	N
	Y		S		R	

66

		Y			C	
	N	O	R	M	A	L
T	A	G			N	
	P	A	N	I	C	
	K			D	E	W
T	I	N	S	E	L	
	N			A		

67

			L			
	W	H	E	A	T	
	A		T		H	
S	T	A	T	I	O	N
	C		E		R	
	H	E	R	O	N	
			S			

68

	G	L	O	V	E	S
	R		W			A
S	A	P	L	I	N	G
	P				O	
M	E	R	M	A	I	D
O			E		S	
P	R	E	T	T	Y	

69

	S	A	U	C	E	
	D		C		O	
W	E	L	C	O	M	E
	G		U		M	
E	R	O	S	I	O	N
	E		E		N	
R	E	A	D	Y		

70

S	U	N	S	E	T	
	N		U		O	
D	I	A	M	O	N	D
	F				I	
C	O	T	T	A	G	E
	R		A		H	
M	I	N	U	T	E	

71

	D			S		
	L	E	N	G	T	H
F	E	E		A		
	T	R	E	A	T	
	T		B	U	G	
T	E	M	P	L	E	
	R			E		

72

			D			
	F	R	O	S	T	
	R		L		H	
A	I	R	P	O	R	T
	E		H		E	
	S	H	I	N	E	
			N			

124

Solutions

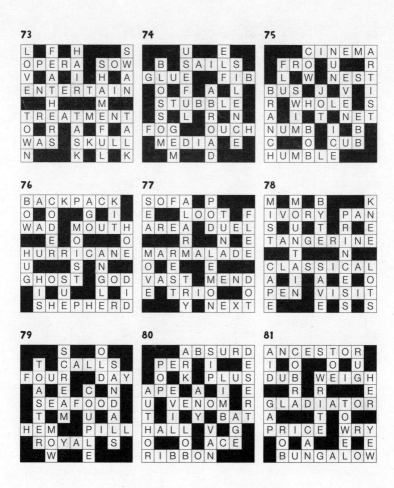

73

```
L   F   H       S
O P E R A   S O W
V   A   I   H   A
E N T E R T A I N
  H     M
T R E A T M E N T
O   R   A   F   A
W A S   S K U L L
N       K   L   L K
```

74

```
    U     E
  B   S A I L S
G L U E   F I B
  O   F   A   L
  S T U B B L E
  S   L   R   N
F O G     O U C H
M E D I A     E
    M       D
```

75

```
      C I N E M A
  F R O   U   R
  L   W   N E S T
B U S   J   V   I
R   W H O L E   S
A   I   T   N E T
N U M B   I   B
C     O   C U B
H U M B L E
```

76

```
B A C K P A C K
O   O   G   I
W A D   M O U T H
    E   O     O
H U R R I C A N E
U       S   N
G H O S T   G O D
  I   U   L   I
  S H E P H E R D
```

77

```
S O F A   P
E     L O O T   F
A R E A   D U E L
    R     N   E
M A R M A L A D E
O   E     E
V A S T   M E N D
E   T R I O     O
    Y   N E X T
```

78

```
M   M   B       K
I V O R Y   P A N
S   U   T   R   E
T A N G E R I N E
    T       N
C L A S S I C A L
A   I   A   E   O
P E N   V I S I T
E     E   S   S
```

79

```
    S   O
  T   C A L L S
F O U R   D A Y
  A   E   C   N
  S E A F O O D
  T   M   U   A
H E M     P I L L
  R O Y A L   S
  W       E
```

80

```
    A B S U R D
  P E R   I   E
  O   K   P L U S
A P E   A   I   E
U   V E N O M   R
T   I   Y   B A T
H A L L   V   G
O     O   A C E
R I B B O N
```

81

```
A N C E S T O R
I   O     O   U
D U B   W E I G H
  R   R     E
G L A D I A T O R
A       T   O
P R I C E   W R Y
  O   A   E   E
B U N G A L O W
```

82

```
H E L P   O
A     L E A D W
M E N U   R U L E
      M   S   E
A T T E M P T E D
L   O   U
S N U G   P U S H
O   R A M P   E
    G   Y A W N
```

83

```
S   T   M       B
H O R S E   E Y E
O   I   A   N   A
E S C A L A T O R
    Y     R
M I C R O W A V E
A   L   N   N   X
S H E   C O C O A
K       E   E   M
```

84

```
      E     N
T   M A G I C
K E E P       B O G
M   I   A     A
P A R E N T S
E   E     S   T
U S E     W E E P
T A B L E R   R
    T     R
```

85

```
      S A M O S A
  B A T   A   U
  A   Y   D R A G
A D S   A   E   U
B   P A S T A   S
S   O   K   L I T
O A T H   E   M
R   I   R A P
B U T T E R
```

86

```
P A R A D I S E
  B   L   N   R
  O R I E N T A L
  V   V   A   I
V E G E T A B L E
O   U   P   A
W O N D E R E D
  D   I   O   L
  D O M I N O E S
```

87

```
V E H I C L E
A   A   O   A   D
L A B   N U R S E
U   I   S       N
A S T R O N A U T
B   N   W   U
L L A M A   A I R
E   L   N   K   E
    L E T T E R S
```

88

```
L   D   C       P
I D E A L   D U E
M   C   U   I   A
P R O F E S S O R
    R       T
S C A R E C R O W
A   T   Y   E   O
F O E   E A S E L
E       S   S   F
```

89

```
W A R M   M
O     A W A Y   G
E X I T   C O A L
      C   G   E
N I G H T M A R E
O   I   E
S O F T   D O Z E
E   T U B A     W
    G   L A C E
```

90

```
A C C I D E N T
I   A       E   I
M I C   A L I E N
    I   L       O
W H I R L W I N D
O       E   G
N A S T Y   L A Y
    T   O   O   E
E N O R M O U S
```